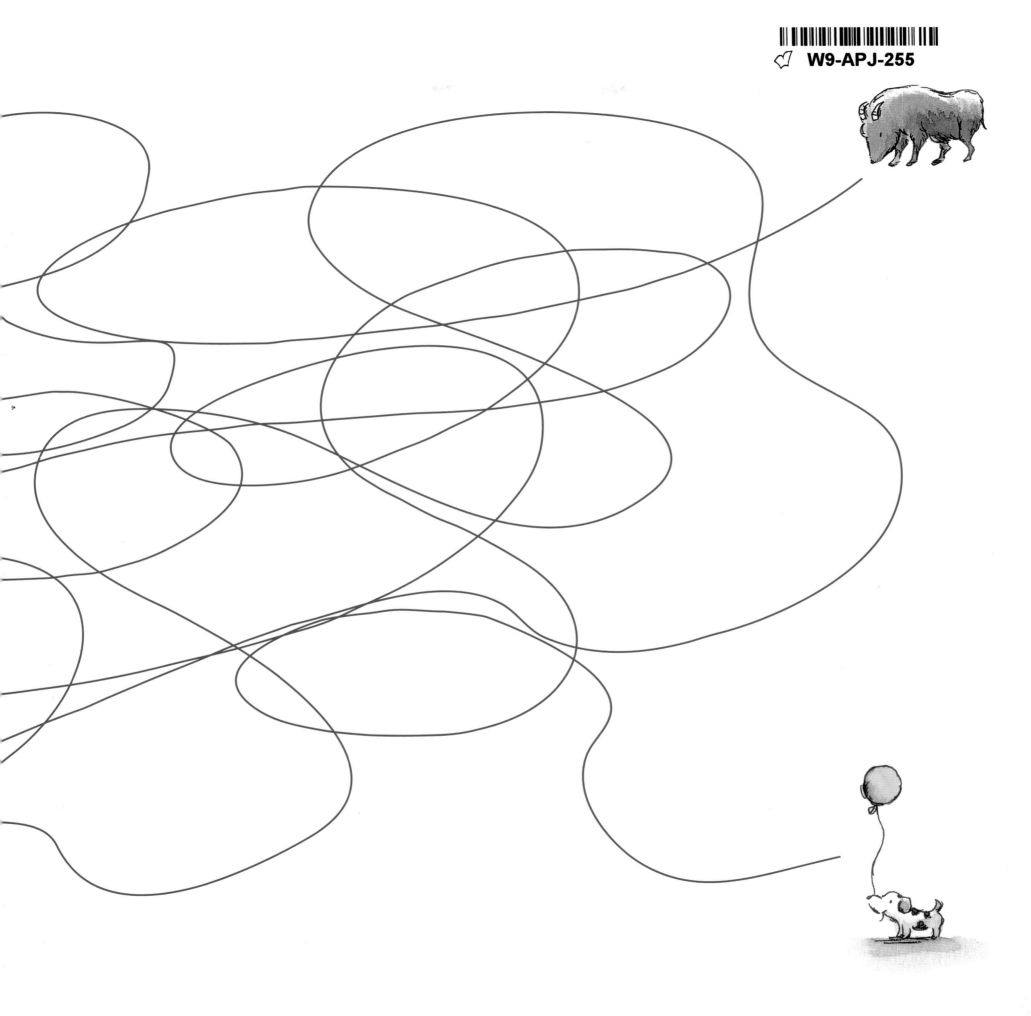

PARIS
HIDE-AND-SEEK

For Theo and all my friends...

Sincere thanks to Isabelle, Laurence, and the whole
Parigramme team, as well as Takako Hasegawa.

PARIS
HIDE-AND-SEEK

MASUMI

TRANSLATED BY ANITA CONRADE

PARIGRAMME

WHEN YOU TAKE THIS TOUR OF PARIS, make sure you keep your eyes peeled. There's so much to see! You'll spot the big monuments first, of course, but if you're a good observer, you'll notice lots of funny details, too.

Let me introduce you to the little boy with the red scarf. He lives in Paris, his name is Theo, and he turns up in every illustration, to play hide-and-seek with you. It's up to you to find him!

But Theo has a dog named Potchi, who keeps running away. You'll be doing Theo a big favor if you spot Potchi's hiding place.

And there's another thing to search for! As you read about the sights of Paris, you'll see a word in **bold**: the name of a special person, animal, or object which is usually a bit out of place!

Use your eagle eyes again to zoom in and point it out. Finally, there's also a yellow balloon floating around the city. Can you spot it, too?

And now it's time to play!

Are you ready, bright eyes?

THE LOUVRE

The Louvre has grown a lot since the Middle Ages, when it was a small fortress. King François I had it rebuilt as a fancy palace in the early 1500s, and then King Henri IV added the long gallery overlooking the Seine. Louis XIV, the Sun King, designed and built the colonnaded façade on the eastern side, Napoleon I incorporated the buildings along the Rue de Rivoli, and Napoleon III, in the 19th century, put the finishing touches on the site. Today, the Louvre is one of the world's biggest museums, if not the biggest. It has wonderful collections of Egyptian, Greek, and Roman antiquities, and paintings by Italian, French, Dutch, and English masters. The most famous one is Leonardo da Vinci's **Mona Lisa**. Hey, she isn't where she belongs... Can you spot her?

PLACE DE LA CONCORDE

This bustling intersection has often been called the world's most beautiful square; in any case, it's the biggest square in Paris. A 3,000-year-old Egyptian obelisk covered with hieroglyphics stands in the center. Ever since 1831, when Egypt gave the obelisk to France, it has been the answer to the riddle, "What's the oldest monument in Paris?" A special ship had to be built to move it across the Mediterranean and up rivers and canals to Paris. Then hundreds of men using winches and pulleys worked to stand it on its pedestal. Perhaps you know that **Egyptian** artists always drew figures with their heads in profile and their torsos facing us. By the way, do you notice anyone unusual taking a stroll here?

THE ARC DE TRIOMPHE
AND THE CHAMPS-ÉLYSÉES

The Arc de Triomphe is a huge structure commissioned by Emperor Napoleon I to represent his victory in the battle of Austerlitz in 1806, when his power was at its peak. However, he was long gone by the time the monument was finished, in 1836. The arch has nevertheless become a symbol of Paris, like the Avenue des Champs-Élysées leading eastward to Concorde. This is where parades are always held on Bastille Day, and it is where Parisians often gather to celebrate important moments in their history. When the French team won the Soccer World Cup in 1998, almost a million people flocked to the Champs-Élysées to revel in the victory together. But one of the players seems to have lost his **ball**! Please join in the search for it.

THE OPERA

The Paris Opera house is a temple dedicated to classical music and ballet. Charles Garnier, the architect who designed it, wanted it to be dazzling and awe-inspiring, and he devoted fifteen years of his life to the project. He ordered the finest marble, columns, sculptures, and mosaics. Inside, there's a majestic stairway leading to the gilded balconies of the auditorium, with its red velvet seats and curtains. The room is a show in itself! The star ballerinas shine on this stage. Imagine this: a young **dance student** is called a "little rat," and she's proud of it! It's because when she prances across the studio floor, her slippers make a sound like a rodent scurrying! Look, I think one of the students is outside in her tutu!

GARE SAINT-LAZARE

Paris's first passenger railway line opened here in 1837. You could board a train and chug all the way to the suburb of Saint Germain-en-Laye. What an adventure! Nowadays, Saint-Lazare is the busiest commuter station in Paris, with 500 000 people bustling through every day. Before the advent of air travel, this station was the most direct route to America! You'd board the train here to Le Havre, where the ship was waiting to steam across the Atlantic. But regardless of your destination, near or far, the main thing is to leave on time, isn't it? There must be a **clock** somewhere in the station!

MONTMARTRE

Montmartre still seems a bit like the country village it was, a couple hundred years ago. It has often been said that there's more Montmartre in Paris than Paris in Montmartre, because this is where the gypsum was quarried, to plaster the walls of all those Paris apartment buildings. Atop its little hill, the village's narrow streets and old-fashioned houses attract throngs of tourists. They, in turn, attract artists of every stripe to the Place du Tertre. Does one of them have a painting of the **Eiffel Tower** for sale?

THE ROOFTOPS of PARIS

The sky contains a multitude of shades of grey, and the rooftops of Paris reflect them. Most of the roofs you see are made of sheets of zinc, but a few have slate shingles. From on high, they look like the ripples in a calm grey lagoon. The city is as vast and beautiful as the ocean, isn't it? And it's so quiet up here, high above the street. The din of the traffic is muted by the time it floats up. Perhaps that's why birds take refuge here. However, they'd better watch out: sometimes a **cat** also steps out for a rooftop prowl.

CANAL SAINT-MARTIN

This canal is a waterway connecting the Bassin de la Villette, in northern Paris, to the Port de l'Arsenal, on the Seine. It opened in 1825. It and Canal Saint-Denis were a handy shortcut for barges plying the meandering Seine. Also, all the bridges downtown were encumbered with pumps and waterwheels, so river navigation was easier here. Today, most of the boats are carrying tourists, not freight. Careful no one falls in the water, or we'll have to throw him a **lifesaver**. Can you find it?

PLACE DE LA BASTILLE

The infamous Bastille prison is gone, but its name remains. In medieval times, it was a fortress defending Paris; later, it was turned into a jail. The king could imprison anybody he felt like, for as long as he felt like. You could get thrown into a dark, dank cell simply for expressing an opinion which differed from the king's. In July 1789, when the French Revolution began, the hated symbol was torn down completely. Now there's a little angel on top of a column in the middle of the circle. He's called the **Genie of Liberty**, and he holds a broken chain in his left hand and a torch in his right. Hey, where did that Genie go?

THE MARAIS

This neighborhood was named hundreds of years ago for the fields and gardens which once flourished in the fertile soil alongside the Seine. Of course, when the King of France decided to build a palace here, things changed. Noblemen and other wealthy people built splendid mansions nearby, to show off their power and elegance. These palaces were neglected for centuries, and some of them were crumbling. Finally, the city took an interest in renovating them, and they were saved from demolition. Nevertheless, these days, lords and ladies are few, and there's little chance you'll see a **carriage**.

L'EPOUVANTAIL

MUSÉE CARNAVALET

This is one of the most beautiful palaces in the Marais. It was built in the 1500s for the wife of a gentleman named Kernevenoy, and, over the years, people began to call it "Carnavalet," instead, because it was easier to pronounce. Nowadays, the mansion houses an exciting museum dedicated to the history of Paris from prehistoric times to the present. This is where the Neolithic cavemen's canoes, found by construction crews at Bercy, are exhibited. There's also a delightful collection of old-fashioned signs from 17th- and 18th-century shops, named for things like nearby trees. For instance, a store that sold hinges and hardware was named for the famous **elm tree** in front of St-Gervais Church.

THE CENTRE POMPIDOU

This big modern building, the Centre Pompidou, has a library, a few auditoriums, and some studios inside, but one of the main things it contains is the national museum of modern art. Usually, architects try to hide plumbing, electricity, and ventilation systems, but Renzo Piano's team proudly displays them, in cheerful colors, on the outside of the building. Green is for water, blue is for air, and yellow is for electricity: you can't get mixed up! The big cobblestone plaza in front of the museum is a regular circus every day: jugglers, guitarists, and mimes vie for the attention of passersby. Sometimes, you may even here a person playing the **violin**…

HÔTEL DE VILLE

This impressive building is Paris City Hall, and has been for a long time – since the 14th century, in fact. Even then, the large open space in front the building was an important gathering place for the people of Paris. They flocked here to look for work, do business, make deals, and hold parades and dances. The first mayor of Paris was named Étienne Marcel, and his statue stands in the garden on the Seine side of the building. It's traditional for the mayors of French towns to wear tricolor red-white-and-blue sashes as symbols of their office. Can you find the mayor's **tricolor sash**?

NOTRE-DAME

The great cathedral is awe-inspiring, with its two tall towers covered with stone sculptures as fine as lace. When Notre-Dame was built a thousand years ago, it was a symbol of the greatness of God and the depth of people's Christian faith. Back then, the statues on the façade were painted in bright colors, but they wore off long ago. The big plaza in front of the cathedral is a modern enhancement. In the Middle Ages, the cathedral was hidden behind blocks of flats, and you'd be surprised by the huge structure just as you turned a corner. But, past and present, there have always been chimes. At least, on days when the **big bell** isn't playing hide-and-seek!

THE BANKS OF THE SEINE

Let's take a stroll along the riverbank, far from automobile traffic. From here, you can spy some of the city's most beautiful monuments as you amble along. It's also fun to wave to the people riding the tour boats, or watch the barges rumbling up and downstream. You may also spot the fast motor launch used by the river police brigade. Many people are fond of this part of Paris: it's a good place to walk a dog, sit on a bench and smooch, or cast a line into the water, hoping to catch something. Where could that **fish** possibly be hidden?

THE ZOO AT JARDIN DES PLANTES

This small zoo is certainly a historical monument, because it was started in 1793 with some exotic animals found in the menagerie at Versailles: a lion, a rhinoceros, and a zebra. A number of homeless bears and monkeys were acquired when a law was passed banning their owners from displaying them in the streets of Paris. Finally, in 1827, the arrival of a giraffe, a gift from Egypt to France, caused a sensation: Parisians thronged the zoo to admire the strange animal. Today, you'll find extensive collections of hawks, reptiles, insects, and amphibians in the menagerie. And I believe a **monkey** has just escaped from his cage!

THE ROMAN ARENA

Almost 2,000 years ago, Paris was called Lutetia. Like the rest of Gaul, it was under Roman rule. Roman builders laid out roads, constructed docks on the river, and built several monuments, including this arena, which could accommodate almost 17,000 spectators. They came to see plays. Sometimes, there was more barbaric entertainment: combats to the death between gladiators, or man versus ferocious beast. In fact, a **lion** is on the loose, so watch out!

LUXEMBOURG GARDENS

These magnificent gardens are the grounds of Luxembourg Palace, which was built for Marie de Medici, who became the second wife of Henry IV in 1600. At the time, the gardens were even bigger than they are today. But there's still plenty of space for you to take a long walk in the fresh air, admiring the statues of the queens of France. Or you may sit in a quiet place to draw… or read… or dream. There's even room for two styles of landscaping: the French garden, with geometrically clipped hedges lining straight walkways, and the English garden, which attempts to imitate nature more faithfully. The wild part of the garden is where you'll find the beehives and beekeeper. But don't worry, even though the honey might attract a **bear**, there aren't any around here.

SAINT-GERMAIN-DES-PRÉS

In the Middle Ages, the biggest monastery in Paris developed in the shadow of the steeple of Saint-Germain-des-Prés Church. It spawned a busy little village, which later became a Paris neighborhood. Though times have since changed, for several decades in the 20th century, the cafés on the boulevard were famous as a gathering places for writers, publishers, and brilliant intellectual trend-setters. Uh-oh, it looks like someone lost a **book**!

ORSAY MUSEUM

Paintings, sculptures, drawings, and photographs: the enormous Orsay Museum is a treasure-house of 19th-century art. It has a large collection of works by the Impressionists, who invented a new theory of painting and even seeing subjects. But did you know that before the building was a museum, it was a train station? Completed in 1900, it was Paris's fanciest train terminal – but within forty years, the platforms turned out to be too short, so it had to be abandoned. It reopened as a museum in 1986, and crowds of art-lovers replaced passengers boarding the **train**.

THE EIFFEL TOWER AND THE CHAMP-DE-MARS

It's impossible to imagine Paris without the Eiffel Tower. When it was built in 1889 by engineer Gustave Eiffel, its 300-meter height made it the tallest manmade structure in the world. It had to be made of iron, because a stone monument this size would collapse under its own weight. At first, people thought the tower was ugly, and started movements to demolish it, but finally, when the telegraph and radio were invented, the tower proved to be extremely useful as an antenna. Today, it's used to beam out television broadcasts. No need to bring your **television set** to the Champ-de-Mars, though: the Eiffel Tower gladly makes home deliveries!

THE ELEVATED METRO

Almost everywhere else in Paris, the subway is a subterranean creature, speeding through its tunnels underneath the city, invisible to surface traffic. You might almost think it didn't exist! But once in a while, it comes out in the daylight, on the elevated lines 2 and 6. These two routes follow boulevards wide enough for both pairs of tracks to fit on the median strip. It's a win-win situation: the cost of digging a tunnel was avoided, and passengers enjoy the benefit of traveling above street level, in the air. That's when you can go from one end of Paris to the other for the price of a single **Metro ticket**.

PLACE DENFERT-ROCHEREAU

Impossible to miss the magnificent king of beasts ruling the square from a pedestal in the middle: it's the Lion of Belfort, symbol of the city of Belfort, in eastern France. The monument honors the way the city's inhabitants resisted the German armies for over one hundred days during the Franco-Prussian War in 1870. Their great courage and the defense strategy implemented by Colonel Denfert-Rochereau prevented the city from falling into German hands when Alsace and Lorraine were lost. A lion this majestic could never be afraid of anyone – certainly not a tiny **mouse**!

VERSAILLES CASTLE

King Louis XIV disliked Paris. As soon as he was crowned, and over the objections of his advisers, he chose a little hunting lodge located in a remote marsh far from the city, and had it enlarged. Then he had the gardens landscaped with fountains, the grand canal, and the basins. Meanwhile, development continued on the castle. Louis XIV wanted to build Europe's largest and most splendid palace, to reflect his omnipotence as the Sun-King. As the seat of France's **crown**, Versailles was also the real capital of the country until the fall of the monarchy.

FRANCE

Direction artistique Isabelle Chemin
Maquette Marylène Lhenri
Édition Mathilde Kressmann

Achevé d'imprimer en UE en juin 2018

Dépôt légal janvier 2009
ISBN 978-2-84096-570-1